The Scrake of Dawn

The Scrake of Dawn

Poems by young people from Northern Ireland

chosen by Paul Muldoon

Blackstaff Press
in association with
The Arts Council of Northern Ireland

Published by Blackstaff Press, 3 Galway Park, Dundonald, Belfast BT16 0AN, in association with the Arts Council of Northern Ireland.

ISBN 0 85640 203 6

Cover photograph by Geraldine Sweeney.
Printed in Northern Ireland by Belfast Litho Printers Limited.

Editor's Note

My thanks are due to the officers of the Arts Council of Northern Ireland who asked me to edit an anthology of poems by young people from the province, in this, the International Year of the Child, and who undertook to invite submissions from every school in Northern Ireland; to the three thousand or so children who responded with such enthusiasm; to the young photographers and to Geraldine Sweeney who helped with the photographs; and, above all, to these eighty young poets who have allowed the rest of us to share their visions at the scrake of dawn.

Paul Muldoon
November 1979.

To Live In Drumbreda

My Family

My Dad just sits there
and reads the newspaper.
My Mum is all get up and go.
My sister sits and studies all day.
My brother thinks only of football.
I often wonder what they think of me.

Mmmmmm. . . . .!

Colin Finnegan (9)
Christian Brothers' Primary School, Armagh.

My Dad

My Dad is stubborn and very lazy.
Every night he buries himself in the newspaper and snores
    like the noise of an elephant;
He likes everybody to do things for him.
He sometimes goes out and comes back all full of laughs and
    giggles, and then falls asleep;
But underneath he is not bad and he's kind and soft hearted.
I like my dad when he is in a good mood.
But when he is in a bad mood his face goes red and he shouts
    and shouts and shouts and then goes off to bed with a sore head.

Joanne Fox (12)
St. Rose's Girls' Secondary School, Belfast.

Never

Mummy says never run onto the road.
Daddy says never cheat.
My brother says never play with his toys.
Nanny says never kiss the boys.
Grandad says never a secret tell.
I'm sick, sore and tired of being told,
      Never!

Rebecca Halliday (8)
Princess Gardens School, Belfast.

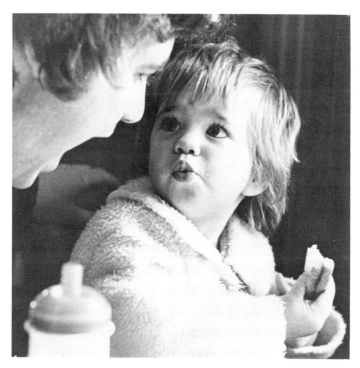

A Box of Matches

On Monday we had no school. And I was in the
house playing with my toys. At dinner time my
mummy said get washed and get clean clothes on
and we will have dinner when daddy comes home.
After tea daddy said to me will you go up to the
shop and get me a box of matches.

Declan Cauldwell (7)
St. Patrick's Primary School, Armagh.

The Inch War

My mum went on a diet,
She said she'd lose some weight.
The spare tyre round her middle
She's tried hard to deflate.

She said her thighs were flabby,
She'd a handsome double chin,
Spare inches round her hipline
No roll-on would keep in.

She got up at six each morning
Her jogging to begin.
Her fight against the inch war
She surely meant to win.

As she counted every calorie
She placed upon her plate,
She wondered if her slimming guide
Had not gone out of date.

She had grapefruit juice for breakfast
Each morning of the week.
Says dad 'Now if she keeps that up
She's sure to look a treat.

'As she jives around the dancefloor
In her size 10 corduroys,
Sure I'll cuddle her and squeeze her
Like when I was a boy'.

The days went quickly rolling by.
I'm so sad to relate
With all her slimming methods
Mum didn't lose much weight.

She just hadn't got the willpower
To shed those extra pounds,
But our home is always jolly
With our 12-stone mum around.

Ailish McSwiggan (11)
St. Mary's Primary School, Drumquin.

Waiting

My mammy is away
to a funeral to say prayers,
but I just sit watching TV and waiting
for my dinner.

Paul Tolan (8)
Holy Cross Boys' Primary School, Belfast.

Frying for Breakfast

Quietly the Cookeen slides down the side of the pan.
Ss Ss Ss Ss the slithery sticky bacon falls noisily into the
    hot greasy pan.
Carefully, I fit in five more pieces of moist bacon.
Patiently, I wait till the bacon is cooked on one side.
Next I turn it with a knife and fork.
When it is crinkled and crisp, I lift the bacon out of the pan.
Hot fat drips off the bacon as I place it on a glass plate in
    the oven.

One by one I crack six eggs into the pan and shake salt
    on them.
Soon I flip the eggs over.
After a while I carefully lift the bubbled eggs onto a plate.
Six yellow eyes stare up at me,
Six crinkled mouths are smiling.

Eight pieces of soda bread now go into the frying pan.
The 'soda' soaks up the Cookeen just like a withered plant
    quenching its thirst.
Quickly I put in more Cookeen.
Next, I turn the pieces of 'soda' with a knife and fork.
When it is brown and crispy I carefully transfer it to the glass
    plate and pile it high.

Then I call for my sleepy-headed sisters
To come and help Mummy, Daddy, Uncle and me
Eat up our hearty breakfast.

Helen C. Brown (10)
Kirkhills Primary School, Ballymoney.

My Granny

My Granny is so good to me —
She gives me sweets and cake —
But every time I want to play
She says she wants to bake.

My Granny wears an old wool shawl
Over a home-made frock.
On one foot is an old grey slipper
On the other just a sock.

My Granny's hair is thick and grey,
She wears it in a bun.
Her body's large, her feet are small.
I'm sure she weighs a ton.

My Granny tells me many cures
She learnt in her young days,
Cures for hiccups or nasty stings
In countless different ways.

When I was young I stayed with her
When Mummy was away,
And when Mum came to pick me up
I begged that I might stay.

My Granny wears a pair of specs
They're thin around the frame.
Her false teeth are too big for her,
But I like her all the same.

Roger Smyth (10)
The Hon. the Irish Society's School, Coleraine.

Acrostic

My aunt invited me over to tea
At twelve o'clock on Saturday morning.
I walked there all the way.
Rosey the maid met me at the door.
Eileen my aunt invited me in.
At tea-time I ate buns and sandwiches.
Daddy came and picked me up at the end.

Mairead Hegarty (9)
Millquarter Primary School, Toomebridge.

The King Went to Visit

The king went to visit
the princess in the castle
and they had a party
and fell in love
and got married
and went to live in Drumbreda.

Joanne Farmer (5)
St. Patrick's Primary School, Armagh.

Enagh Milford

Not 'Milford' the few streets outside Armagh
But 'Enagh, Milford',
A few houses outside 'Milford',
An isolated unknown, unexplored area,
But still there.
I know it.
Daddy knows it.
But do you?
I doubt it.
You know 'Milford', a few streets,
But do you know 'Enagh, Milford',
A few houses?

Diarmuid O'Hare (11)
St. Patrick's Primary School, Armagh.

My Surroundings

The street where I live is called Glencairn Pass.
It's beside the mountains all covered in grass.
Bees buzz around and cows moo all day
And all the children ever do is play, play, play.

The mountains are a beautiful sight,
But all the people ever do is fight.
The birds make nests in the trees,
And flowers give nectar to the honey bees.

All night lights shine,
And all looks fine,
But out in the towns people fight,
And kill with all their might.
Birds don't chirp,
And flowers don't smile,
And men line up in a single file.

Lynn Murray (12)
Everton Girls' Secondary School, Belfast.

Bring Your Friend

Play-School

It's nine o'clock this Tuesday morning
When the infants go to school.
Through the door they all come rushing
To find their favourite toy.
At ten o'clock they have their orange
And usually a biscuit too.
At eleven o'clock their mums collect them
To bring them home to watch T.V.

Robert Leitch (11)
Olderfleet Primary School, Larne.

16

Noises at Day

The bang of long transport lorries as they go
    over bumps and large stones.
The yelling of the master's voice takes the breath
    out of my mouth.
The banging of cutlery in the dinner hall,
And worst of all that terrible bell.
The flickering of pages gives me the creeps.
The scraping of pens on paper I suppose is something
    to get used to.
Big long faces is a common sight,
After the whack of the ruler makes contact with
    their hands.

Philip Murphy (12)
St. Patrick's Primary School, Armagh.

The Playground

The field was wet and wasn't used to-day, so the
boys played football in the playground.
After tuckshop I went down to lean against
Miss Hicks' classroom and watch, but already
Mark Curran and J.P. were there so I went
over to the other side to Sharon Toal, to talk to her
and try to score but I knew I had no chance.
John McKeever was taking a corner on the other side
and the boys and Sandy were standing, arms up, shouting
'Johnny, Johnny here'.
The bell clangs. A few of the boys jog away.
Sandy shouts 'Quick Johnny!'
But Mr. McBride knocks the ball out of his hands,
throws it to Sheamie Connolly saying 'Put it away'.
The playground slowly clears,
the lines disappear into classrooms.
Michele Leer, Maeve Corrigan and Sarah Grimley
stay to pick up the papers.

Michele McSorley (11)
St Patrick's Primary School, Armagh

Break-time

The bell has gone, it's break-time now.
Out to the playground for another row.
Soon a crowd has gathered round.
I throw my opponent to the ground.
I raise my boot to kick him hard
When a master appears in the yard.
As quick as a flash I run away,
But I'm found out at the end of the day.
The master gives me a thousand lines to write
But that won't stop me from the break-time fight.

Donal Kelly (13)
St Joseph's High School, Coalisland.

Alone

The time has come.
My nerves await.
My mammy leaves the school I hate.

I stand alone
And everybody looks.
'What's the matter' I ask,
'I've got my pens and books.'

The teacher comes through
And slams the door.
'Hello children' she says.
My head droops to the floor.

The bell has gone,
I still await.
But a girl comes over.
Her name is Kate.

Brenda O'Toole (12)
St Rose's Girls' Secondary School, Belfast.

Play-time

I call for my friend who lives next door.
We go out for an hour or more.
'Let's go on our bikes' my friend says to me.
'We shall go for a ride up Clon-lee.'

When we are back we play two balls,
But very soon my mother calls,
'It's time for tea. You had better come.
Bring your friend and she can have some.'

Joanna McGarel (10)
Olderfleet Primary School, Larne.

The Coke

I stand staring,
as Gary raises the bottle,
wishing he will ask me if I want a drink.
A pleading expression forms on my face,
but no words leave his mouth.
Two pursed lips open.
'Ah . . .' he sighs.
The bottle drops,
and he wipes from above his mouth
a coke moustache.

Brian Kirk (11)
St Patrick's Primary School, Armagh

Accident Prone

My wee brother took a bottle and he fell
and the bottle smashed.
He got his face bandaged up.
I thought he was a mummy.

My Granda taught me to box and the next day
we had a fight and I broke his arm and he
had to go to hospital.

Martin Daly (6)
St Patrick's Primary School, Armagh

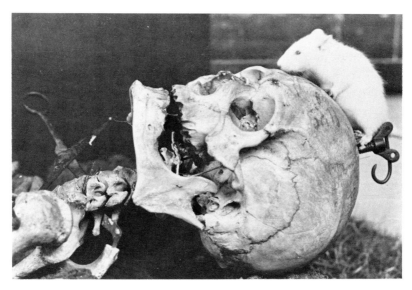

23

Cluedo

'Do you want to play Cluedo?'
I said to my friend.
'All right'
She answered,
'I'll set it out'
And off she went to fetch the board.

'Is everything ready now?'
I asked.
'Yes, now let's start. You throw first'
My friend said.
'Oh good, I've thrown a six.
I'm in the lounge.
I suspect Mrs Peacock killed Dr Black
in the lounge with the dagger'
I said.
'Can you show me anything?'
'Yes' my friend answered,
'Look'.
'Oh, right. Thanks. Your go'
I said.
'I'm in the study.
I suspect Rev Green killed Dr Black in
the study with the rope'
said my friend.
'Anything to show?'
'No'
I said.

'I accuse Rev Green of killing Dr Black
in the study with the rope.
Am I right?'
'Oh good
Let's have another game'
I said.

Tabitha Logan (9)
Leadhill Primary School, Belfast.

The Attic War

The attic was full of planes,
models scattered about the
room. Every size and shape
from a F.W. 190 to a Short
Sterling, every one painted
and ready for a raid.

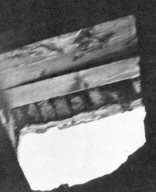

I pictured the scene, a
propeller starts to roar,
then another and another
until a scream of pistons
echoes in the hanger, a
heavy bomber taxis
and lines up for take-off.

One after one the nose tilts
upwards and the armed monster
takes to the air. A monstrous
drone fills the air, then a small
dot dives from the sun and sweeps
in low, nose-guns red hot.

A nimble hand on the controls
saves a bomber from certain
destruction. The rear bombers
open fire on the small fighter.
Dodging a terrible hail of fire the
pilot takes a shot at a sluggish
Stirling isolated from the pack,
the right inner engine flares up
into a ball of fire.

Suddenly a voice comes over the
intercom. No, it's my mother
calling for the third time, come
and get your lunch.

Ian McClure (11)
Stranmillis Primary Schoool,
Belfast.

Like Me

Did Jesus play tig and climb trees
or make faces at girls?
Did Jesus play with action men
or play with toy cars?
Did Jesus draw funny little cars or pretend
he was the six million dollar man?
Did Jesus do these things like me?

Did Jesus play basketball
or climb a coalshed roof?
Was Jesus in a football team
or in the cubs or scouts?
Did Jesus play cricket in the garden
or camp out?
Did Jesus do these things like me?

Declan Keenan (10)
St Patrick's Primary School, Armagh.

The Hole in the Fence

A glimpse through a hole in the fence,
And I suddenly hear children's voices.
Mixed children playing together.
Children resting on the warm footpath
Puffing and panting
After a long and tiring game of skips.
Some other children
Sat in the shade of a huge tree
Eating ice-lollies
And flies and bees buzzing round them.
Some children playing tig,
Catching each other,
Shouting and yelling as they pass.
Then the voices died away.
The children had gone
Except for one small boy.

Maxine Alcorn (11)
Forth River Primary School, Belfast.

The Door Opens

The Refuse Collectors

Every Monday morning at seven o'clock
The refuse collectors come and give me a shock.
One shouts 'Here Bill number 30 now'
And Mrs Jones comes out and creates a big row.

Now they're emptying the bins with such a clatter
But all the noise they make to them doesn't matter.
They are going now, oh what a relief,
But they'll be back in another week.

Fionnuala Smyth (9)
St Bride's Primary School, Belfast.

The Carrot Woman

The carrot woman is tall and thin,
She has green hair,
And long orange body,
Broad at the top
And narrow at the bottom.

She sits at her stall
In the market place,
Summer or winter,
Rain or shine.
She sells fruit and vegetables.

Her customers are many and loyal.
Each week they buy her goods.
They know that the best will be given to them
Because they are always fresh and clean.

Mairead Devlin (12)
St. Rose's Girls' Secondary School, Belfast.

A Visit to the Dentist

I mount the steps, one, two, three,
Wishing this person wasn't me.
I check out my name and step aside,
Sorry I'm here and trying to hide.
Too soon it's my turn.
I walk to the room.
My heart is beating like a spoon.
I open my mouth
Resigned to my fate.
'All sound' said the dentist,
'Let's fix your next date.'

Edwina Chambers (9)
Ashley House School, Belfast.

Bead in my Ear

One time I got a bead in my ear. The City Hospital could
do nothing so I had to go to Craigavon. When we were in the
ambulance the man told me the windows had one-way glass.
The doors at the entrance opened automatically.
The ward smelled of tonic and after-shave as well as Avon.
It seemed as if my head had just touched the pillow when
I was woken by a shuffling near my bed.
A hard-looking sister stood there with ginger hair,
mean eyes, stern mouth and bossy tongue.
Later a nurse took me to the hall where I was to go for
the operation. I felt like wheeling the bed to another door.
Doc Sleepy gave me an injection in the knuckle. I did not
feel anything.
A few days later I went home.

Tonia Smith (8)
St Patrick's Primary School, Armagh.

Hairdresser's

The door opens, I walk in, take a seat.
Everyone is staring,
large eyes getting brighter.
You feel like an animal, a dog with a swollen paw.
Women are chatting,
heads nodding, mouths moving.

It is like a dog show.
In corners bubbly heads are popping up,
heads like gollies, faces like moons.
Others are getting their hair painted,
black, blonde, ginger and even blue.
'Next please.'

You sit at a mirror unable to speak,
as well as look.
You sit with a face like a tomato
and come out with a baldy head.
You are being discussed by young and old.
'That's £1.50 please.'
You walk out with a baldy head and a face like a moon.

Joanne Breen (16)
Lurgan Technical College

34

Silage Making

Silage time is here again,
When all the farmers get a pain,
And if it happens to rain
All the work goes down the drain.

Cutting and mowing in neat rows
Up the harvester spout it goes.
This goes on to the end of May
And then it's time to make hay.

David McCalmont (10)
Ballypriormore Primary School, Islandmagee.

Raspberry and Crab Apple Jelly
Greenvale, Autumn '77

I remember
the tart, bright-red jam on Marie biscuits.
You brought it out to us while we
Dug nettle roots and cleared the long grass.

I remember
The strong sun, the flies, the perfect calm,
The weeds and sturdy dock-leaf roots.
As bending, heaving, we pulled away
To clear jungle from the canes and bushes
To allow the growth of next summer's harvest of berries
To make next autumn's jelly and jam.

Suzanne Bell (17)
Cookstown High School.

All Of Us Folk Who Quack

The Tom Cats' Male Voice Choir

Just as you're getting over to sleep
Out from their hideouts they quietly creep.
Their timing is perfect, they know when you tire,
And it's then they begin their cat's Male Voice Choir.

The first one starts off with a series of screams
Then slowly and painfully you're roused from your dreams.
The second cat follows in a series of moans,
As you rise from your bed with a series of groans.

You search for the boot you used last night,
The one with the greatest power,
To hurl at those cats that woke you up
At this unearthly hour.

Slowly and quickly you open your window,
Get ready to aim, then fire.
Out from your hand the boot goes
Whizzing into the cold night air.

Your aim was perfect,
And your weapon landed right on the leader's head.
They've all disappeared. Peace at last!
Time to get back to bed.

Eileen McGhee (13)
Kilkeel High School.

Cats

I have two cats
One white, one grey
They play in the garden all day
They sit at my side when I am going
To ride a bicycle on my own.

They follow me in the snow
And I do not know
Where one goes
Because it is white.

Eilish O'Donnell (12)
Millquarter Primary School, Toomebridge.

41

The Noises at Night

At night,
when my brothers and sister are asleep
I hear the mice scampering across the attic floor.
I think to myself
They will pull all the feathers off
my daddy's stuffed birds.

Dominick Vallely (8)
Christian Brothers' Primary School, Armagh

A Hen

A hen is like a wren,
Sometimes they live in a pen.
They have plenty of feathers
And they are like leather

Owen Roe O'Donnell (8)
Millquarter Primary School, Toombridge.

The Hawk

Emerging from shadow into autumnal sunlight,
Wheeling, gliding, the hawk displays through flight its
    mastery of the air.
Small, light body, tapered wings and flat, square tail,
It is perfectly formed for high-diving — its speciality.
From above its tawny-brown back blends perfectly with the
    dry, dead bracken.
But from below it is a caramel-coloured missile which strikes
    the target
With infinite dexterity.
After hours of this tireless flight the hawk perceives its prey—
A defenceless racing pigeon,
Then, as if from nowhere, it plummets like a stone with
    tremendous speed.
It strikes the unfortunate pigeon with lethal outstretched
    talons.
Instantaneously the inferior bird dies, its neck broken.
Grey and white feathers disperse and flutter slowly
    downwards.
The triumphant hawk feeds, eyes glinting like polished
    armour search suspiciously,
Replete — once again it soars upwards.
One small bloodstained feather sinks in the eddy of rushing
    air from the powerful wings.

Anne Kinney (15)
Dominican College, Belfast

43

The Prayer of the Little Ducks

Dear God give us plenty of water,
Give us plenty of slugs to eat,
Protect all of us folk who quack.
                    Amen.

Amanda Hoey (10)
Ballykeel Primary School, Ballymena.

44

Seaweed

It lies like a monster
With hair all green and lumpy,
With witches' hands crawling
Trying to reach you.
It is slimy and slippery
Smelling like salt.
It looks like old nettles
That have stung themselves
And come out in lumps.

Patrick McAweaney (12)
St. Patrick's Boys' Secondary School, Cookstown.

45

My Dog

Small and brown,
A tail like a snake,
Frisky and jumpy like a wild horse,
Fast as a greyhound,
Hunts like a fox,
And plays football like Kenny Dalglish.

The Shark

The shark, sleek and grey,
Ruler of the sea.
He prowls, silently, through his dark kingdom.
A small, bright fish, like a star in the dark night.
The shark slowly follows it.
Unsuspecting, peaceful, the little fish darts along.
A quick movement, gone in a flash.
The little star of the sea goes out.

Sean McKegney (13)
Rathmore Grammar School, Finaghy.

The Frog

Slimy, greasy, Olympic jumper,
Leaping, springing, flying through the air.

No numbered T-shirt on his back,
To leap the hurdles on the track,
No crowd to watch his brilliant spring,
Just other frogs who do the same thing.

Sheelagh Carville (12)
St. Dominic's High School, Belfast.

The Goldfish

It can swim with ease
One flip of its fin
Moves it speedily along
It swims round the bowl
Like a dog chasing a cat
Around a bin lid.

Stephen Jeffrey (11)
Elmgrove Primary School, Belfast.

Gums

Gums is our fish at school,
We have birds and gerbils too.
I think Gums is the best.
We named him Gums
Because he had no teeth,
He swims around his home like a shark,
Guarding all his valuable things.

Andrew McDuff (11)
Olderfleet Primary School, Larne.

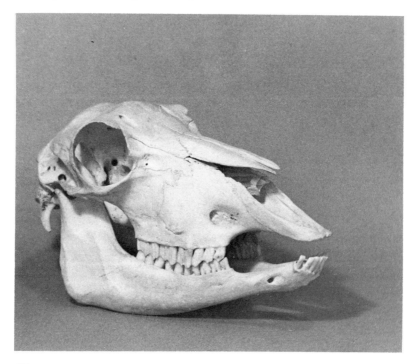

Country Sounds

In the evening I stand still,
Listening to the baby crows.
They be sitting in their nests in the trees
Squealing like rats.
Down below I hear the Clady burn rushing over the weir,
Into the pool below.
I hate looking down on the weir,
It makes me dizzy
But I like the roar of the water
In the morning.
I hear the hens cackling.
They want out for grain.
Darkie miaows on the window sill
And scrabs the pane.
She's hungry.
John Oan Roe's van zooms up
To call for Daddy,
Brakes screeching as he turns on the gravel.
Dan O'Hara is out shouting at his dog.
He's wild cross with him.
Late in the evening the Charolais bull routs at the cows
When Daddy drives them to Inispollen for milking.
And the gate creaks,
It always creaks when it's not tied.

Patricia McCurdy (10)
St. Ciaran's School, Cushendall.

A Monster

A monster wrecked our school.
The monster looked like a hat with hairy eyes and ten legs with bones that rattled. His hands were made out of bracelets. He hid in Mrs O'Hare's cupboard. Mrs O'Hare went past the cupboard and the monster followed her. The whole class threw the monster into a bucket of water.

Vultures

I hate vultures because they would nip me.
They have big sharp beaks to nip me with and it would hurt. Vultures are very dangerous because when cowboys are going to die the vultures fly about and when the cowboys die the vultures eat them.

Celine Kelly (6)
St. Patrick's Primary School, Armagh.

The Cows in the Meadow

'Hello' said the Jersey Cow
To the Friesian one
'It's a wonderful day
Just look at the sun'
'Aye' the Friesian cow replied,
'The weather on "Good Evening Ulster" for to-morrow was
  bad'
'Oh!' said the Jersey Cow 'I was watching "Scene Around
  Six"'
'Where's wee Toby by the way?'
'He's over by the hay ricks'
'Who are you on for in the election?'
Said the Jersey.
'I'm on for Maggie Thatcher'
'Oh, good so am I'
'Hey! where's my Jill, I'd better catch her'
'No, look there she is with Kelly'
'Oh, thanks. Honestly these we'ans'
'Oh! wait till I tell you Toby has a sore belly'
'Poor wee lad'
'He has an appointment with Mr Sammer'
'Hey is Toby going to Greenland or Grammar?'
'Do you have the time on you?'
'My watch is in the jeweller's'
'You don't need my watch to know the time, look there's the
  farmer!'
'It's 7.30 time for milking. Take a look!'
'Oh. Yes, Toby come here, you too Duke'

Pamela McCluskey (11)
Olderfleet Primary School, Larne.

The Birds

The birds go to a warm country in winter
and they come back to us in spring.
They sing doodle-doodle in the trees every morning.

Patricia Oliver (6)
St. Patrick's Primary School, Armagh.

Feeding Pheasants

The pheasants are waiting.
They are standing crowing loudly
Letting themselves be heard.
They know it's feeding time
As I push the scoop into the grain bucket,
Pull it out full,
The grain dropping off it like snow falling from the sky,
As I place the lid on the bucket.
The lock's waiting to be opened on the aviary door.
It opens with a push
With the hinges screeching in the same tone as usual.
Here the pheasants come in the same rage as everyday.
'Come on, come on', I shout,
As I throw the grain among the roots
As they scratch and scrape like a digger removing top-soil.
Now I'm lifting the briars to check for eggs
For to set under bantams.

Mervyn Hylands (16)
Lurgan Technical College.

The Badger Hunter

Out on the hills in the evening
Is where and when you would see Jim Smith
The badger hunter
Plodding along with a gun over his shoulder
And an empty sack on his back.
His little terriers follow close behind
Trying to pick up the scent of badgers.
When they smell a badger
A lot of barking is their signal,
They run to the entrance of the set
Followed by Jim.

Down the set he sends his dogs
To seek the badgers.
Jim's ear touches the ground
Like a metal detector
To hear where the dogs are,
Fighting the badgers.

Then he has to dig down
Until he strikes his gold, the badger.
Then up with his shot-gun
He squeezes the trigger gently
And that brings an end to the badger.

Then he starts all over again
To find another one.
When the evening is over
Out across the hills
You see him head for home
With a gun on his shoulder
And a full sack on his back.

Allan Croskery (14)
Quoile High School.

The Dog

His beady eyes peered out from his shaggy black coat
As he barked his frightening cry.
His ears were pricked as he listened for an answering call.

John McConville (10)
St. Malachy's Primary School, Armagh.

It's Got To Come Sometime

Noise

Noise is a terrible thing,
It gives us a headache sometimes,
Even if you're a King.

Noise can be an aeroplane,
Noise can be the sea,
Noise can be as soft as rain.

Noise can be children playing in a room,
It can be as gentle as snow,
Noise can be leaves brushing on the roof.

Noise can be money jingling in a purse,
It can be wind blowing,
It can even be a nurse.

Alison Green (8)
Princess Gardens School, Belfast.

The Cellar

Down deep in the cellar
Where nobody ever goes,
There's a world of evil
Right beneath your feet.

You might stay awake all night,
Never to get to sleep.
Beneath you in the cellar
The rats of death may be discussing you.

Deep down in the cellar
Only once a year
The Demon comes to visit.
He leaves his trail of death.

If you haven't got a cellar
You might think all for the better,
But up above you in the attic
Life is even worse
Than down deep in the cellar.

Paula Crickard (9)
St. Nicholas' Girls' Primary School, Carrickfergus.

60

White

White is peaceful
White is an old man in a rocking-chair
White is the colour of the sky
And of ghosts going through the air.

Philip McIroy (8)
Holy Cross Boys' Primary School, Belfast.

The Rainbow

A scarf that keeps the sky warm.
A half circle painted rich colours.
A crooked zebra-crossing in the sky.
The road to paradise where the sun never ends.

Paul Lowe (8)
Holy Cross Boys' Primary School, Belfast.

High Diving

Walking, slowly,
Like a condemned man
About to die
Trying to look brave
My head held high.

Standing, waiting,
Anxiously wanting
To make the dive,
Hoping, praying that I'll
Still be alive.

Gracefully diving,
Hitting the water
Then skimming past
A streaming white sheet,
Surfacing at last.

Rosemary Henderson (14)
Sacred Heart of Mary Grammar School, Holywood.

Sadness

I don't like the word called sadness. I don't like the meaning too. Sadness is to me when I am bored and tired and have nothing to do. When I am sad I have a big lump in my throat and I can't help crying, I think sadness has broke out. But my dad soon shuts me up he says 'Stop moaning or I'll give you a clout.'
I hate being sad but it's got to come sometime.

Sarah O'Brien (11)
Stranmillis Primary School, Belfast.

Climbing Everest

My mum bought a paper one day,
The paper was the *Daily Mail*.
When she had read it she gave it to me
And I started to read the advertisements page.

I spotted an advertisement,
'Climber wanted, age about thirty'.
I wonder if I would be allowed,
I'm thirty-one and have had experience.

I read the advertisement over again,
'Apply to the Mount Hill climbing centre'
'Ho, Ho,' I thought 'That's only a mile away,
I'll go and pack my snow gear'

Soon I was ready with all my gear,
So I set off in my rusty old car
'What do you want?' said the man at the desk.
'I've come to apply to climb Everest'

'Climb aboard this plane sir. It's going to Nepal'
After hours of boring flying,
'This is Nepal we're coming to,
We will be landing very soon'

Bump! The wheels have touched the ground,
'Everyone out, we start to climb in three days' time'
Three days later the head man says
'Out of bed, we're going to start climbing'

Up the mountainside we go,
Base camp is only a mile away,
Soon we reach it with time to spare
'We could start out to camp one now' said the headman.

So we started, and as the days passed
We arrived at camp one and made a mess.
Camp two we made with the loss of a man.
Camp three was small, the food was terrible.

When we reached camp four we were tired,
And when camp five was reached we were drenched.
Later on we started with our oxygen to the summit.
After hours of exhausting climbing the summit could be seen.

As we reached the summit the oxygen was running out.
'Make for camp five and hurry' said the headman to the men.
After hours of boring descent, we finally started home.
The plane took off and Everest was left behind.

Simon Maguire (11)
Olderfleet Primary School, Larne.

America

I am very excited because in a fortnight I'm going to
America.
Sometimes I think what would happen if the plane crashed.
It would be on the news and in the papers
A plane had crashed in the Atlantic ocean.
My parents would be in a panic.
I wonder has she survived?

Yesterday a plane fell into the sea.
A four-inch bolt had come off the wing
And hundreds of people were drowned,
So with some excitement and worry in my heart
I will go to America.

Marie-Therese Martin (10)
St. Anthony's Girls' Convent School, Belfast.

Subway

I go underground sometimes when I want to cross the road.
I go down steps and then up steps.
It is a safe way to cross the road.
I think it is called a subway.

Richenda Smyth (6)
St. Patrick's Primary School, Armagh.

Graffiti in the Subway

He was the hardman, society drop-out,
Mixing with an unsavoury gang
Whose life comprised of broken boots, borstal sentences
And hanging around with the boys.
His outer self was impenetrable, tough,
His inner self struggled alone and
Expressed his thoughts on the subway walls.
Father a drunk, mother ditto,
They tried to give him a chance but failed.
A shandy tin provided the evening's enjoyment.
First its contents. The clatter on the pavement told the rest.
The morning had gained him a pocketful of crisp notes.
Police-radios buzzed staccato with information,
But all the while his anonymity prevailed,
And yelled out on the subway walls.

Anne Kinney (15)
Dominican College, Belfast.

The Punk down our Street

He has chains through his leather jacket,
A pin through his ear, a dog collar round his neck,
An ear-ring through his ear and combed-back hair.
But I don't like punks, Teds are best.

John Woods (8)
Holy Cross Boys' Primary School, Belfast.

Fat Poof

One day I was walking home from school and all I heard was 'Fat Poof' from the other side of the road.

There was a small lad on a bicycle. He was about eight years old. He repeated this gesture again and again. I got fed up and walked over onto the same side of the road as him and digged him in the arm. A sudden cry of pain came from him and he said 'Fat Poof' again. He was holding his bicycle in front of him. I pushed down on the pedal and he jerked forward and fell down on the top of his bicycle. I walked off and left him there.

I was really proud of what I had done. When I got home I told Dad. He said 'Quick thinking Batman'.

Adrian Leonard (11)
Stranmillis Primary School, Belfast.

Graffiti

While standing waiting for a train
I find out that Joe loves Jill,
Linfield are going to win the cup,
A premonition from Bill,
Judith's got a broken heart,
Buffer's got one again!
Martin's drawn a great big sign
Reading 'Please come back, Jane'
Ian Dury for P.M.
I agree with that, don't you?
Well, if you can't beat them, join them,
So Laura she loves, who?

Laura McKenna (13)
Sacred Heart Grammar School, Holywood.

Labour Party Under Pressure

Now it's a 40% claim
The ambulance threat is spreading.
Unions involved in pay talks
Just what way are things heading?

Industry virtually grinds to a halt
Fuel striking drivers no decline
Haulage men call for all out strike
Maybe Callaghan will resign.

David Brendan Arthur (15)
Faughan Valley Secondary School, Cross.

You Said

You said we would leave together,
take our chance and run.
You said we could fly together,
take our love and run.

You said we would find some place
where we could hide.
The world owes us that much space.
It gives us a chance to get inside.

You said you hadn't much money,
I know I haven't a lot.
You said it didn't matter,
we could survive on what we'd got.

But could we go much further?
I'm so scared of being caught.
I hate these people, this place,
this world, much more than I had thought.

Ursula Kelly (15)
Assumption Grammar School, Ballynahinch.

Chivalry

Where have the days of chivalry gone?
They seemed so merry and gay,
A man if he met you in the street
Would take off his hat and say 'Good Day'.

A man if going through a door
Would open it and let you go before,
He wouldn't mind what your face looked like
He would open it for it was considered polite.

Or if you were standing on a bus
He would get up without a fuss,
He wouldn't mind what his friends might say
Because it was considered the thing in their day.

But now chivalry's dead and gone
Only a few still carry it on.
A man now if he met you in the street
You can be sure wouldn't be so discreet.

A man if going through a door
Would slam it, and let you fall to the floor.
And if your face looked a little bit plain
He'd go back and do it again!

Or if you were sitting in a bus
He would get up and make a fuss.
He'd make sure his friends heard what he had to say
But first he'd make sure it went your way.

Well all this just goes to say
You can't have chivalry and equal pay!

Carol McKee (16)
Everton Girls' Secondary School, Belfast.

75

Friends

When
you introduced me
to life
I met some of
your other friends too.
The sun,
the moon
and happiness.

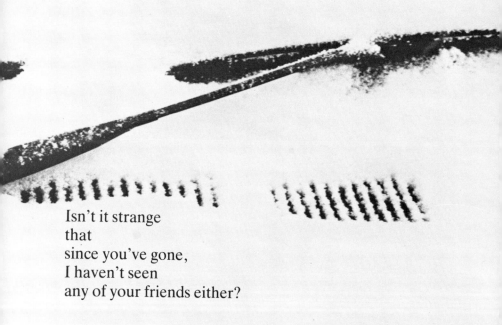

Isn't it strange
that
since you've gone,
I haven't seen
any of your friends either?

Jacki Elliott (16)
Dalriada School, Ballymoney.

Two People

They walk hand in hand
lovers for now, fighters later,
talking about intimate things,
families, how much they love each other,
how they make each other happy,
but as soon as the ring is on her finger,
they change,
bickering and fighting all the time.

Donna Forsythe (16)
Lurgan Technical College

The Mermaid

Upon a white rock sits a mermaid
Comb within her hand
She is so sweet and beautiful
I wish that she could stand.

Her hair is shiny and so golden
Eyes so clear and blue
She sings the sweetest lullabyes
Just for me and you.

And as our ship passes by
I see her dive below
The sea so snowy white with foam
Her head the last to go.

Elaine Montgomery (11)

Paradise Island

Maybe you've been to Timbuktoo,
Or maybe you've been to Waterloo,
But I've been to a place where no one has gone,
I've been to Paradise Island at the scrake of dawn.

The sea is silver
The sand is gold
The food is exotic
And the tall trees are bold.
There's music playing,
And dancers swaying,
On Paradise Island at the scrake of dawn.

Gillian McConnell (11)
Olderfleet Primary School, Larne.

Goll Mac Morna

Goll Mac Morna
His only eye unblinking,
Cunning, courageous and wise.
He sits beside the flickering fire gazing to a moonlit sky.
He's thinking of battles,
Some he had won and those he had lost.

Jason Doherty (9)
Christian Brothers' Primary School, Armagh.

Snow

The snow was here not long ago
And it's very cold as well.
As I walked out in the snow one day
I tumbled over and fell.

The snow makes every place nice and bright,
You can see every track made at night.
We built a big snowman one night.
We made him nice and smoking a pipe.

When the sun came, away he went,
And all that was left was his great big print.

Patricia Scullion (9)
Millquarter Primary School, Toomebridge.

If I Was The Head Of It

The Lost Years

They talk, the older folks,
And paint a rosy past.
Oh! I am tired of hearing
How things were in Belfast.

They talk and tell me stories
Of the good times they once had
And the more they talk about it all
The more it makes me sad.

For I cannot remember
A childhood free from strife,
To me the bombs and bullets
Are just a way of life.

So I have just one question
To ask our violent men.
What about my wasted childhood,
Can you bring it back again?

Fionnuala Bogues (16)
Dominican Convent, Belfast.

Where I Live.

Stray dogs lying in old dirty streets.
Some are dying of hunger.
Cars are stolen and driven speedily away
Onto the road, swerving to avoid innocent people.

Bottles are getting smashed,
Windscreens are getting bottles thrown through them.
You can hear people shut their windows with a loud bang
And you can hear water rushing through the pipes
When next door's neighbour wants a cuppa.
At night you can hear footsteps through unwelcoming
    corridors,
And a muffled sound of families talking.

Eileen Murphy (9)
St. Comgall's Girls' Primary School, Belfast.

Belfast

Belfast is where I was born
I could not bear to leave
But if I really had to
I certainly would grieve.

The things I would miss about it
Are the streets and the City Hall
With cars driving and beeping their horns
And buildings that are so tall.

I'll never, ever leave it
It's my home for evermore
And if I was the head of it
I'd stop this stupid war.

Colm Hearty (10)
St. Bride's Primary School, Belfast.

St Patrick

St. Patrick I know you help us in very many ways
But now comes the time to help us in these days
The fighting starts in Belfast
And works its way to Dublin
I'm afraid it's not snakes
It's fighting that's our problem.

Paul Laverty (6)
St. Bride's Primary School, Belfast.

The Shankill

The rag and bone man slowly makes his way around with his old horse and cart.

The roundabout has stopped playing. The old happy tunes have faded away, they are thought of no more. The new money has taken over and left the old folk in a fluster wondering if 2/3 is the same as 13p. The wars they said were over, but were they? Were the wars all over so that no more fighting would take place on the Shankill?

The Shankill it used to be a nice place. Not any more. Old blocked-up buildings or burned-out pubs, or a few dirty kids roaming the streets with nowhere to go and nothing to do. Plastic bullets flying from one side to another, fighting seems to be the main sport on the Shankill nowadays. Tramps lying in doorways, drunks lying on steps and the old woman trying to cross the road.

Ann Devine (12)
Everton Girls' Secondary School, Belfast.

Come to Belfast.

Come to Belfast,
That beautiful, polluted, bullet-ridden Belfast.
Come and get frisked by the security man
At the airport,
Actually get your car checked
By real live soldiers,
And then drive in the guerilla-infested countryside.
But if you would prefer the city,
Why not take a bus to the riots
And join in the stone-throwing,
Or even stop to have a chat with
The bomb disposal experts in action.
Spend a week in the barbed wire surrounded Europa,
And if you're lucky, you'll get a petrol bomb chucked
Through your window.
Once in a while you'll get stopped by a terrorist road block,
Or even catch a glimpse of a car blowing up.
All in all your stay in Belfast will be a peaceful
and well-spent holiday that you'll never forget.

Geoffrey Smyth (13)
Rathmore Grammar School, Belfast.

A Rock Concert in Belfast.

Rule the Roost
Have left the stage
At long last for we want Rory.
The lights go down
A spotlight flicks on
The moment we've been waiting for.

Gerry McAvoy and Ted McKenna
Bassist and drummer of the trio
Start up the rhythm of 'Shin Kicker'
Then comes Rory
With sunburst finish battered stratocastar
Round his neck, still soundin' good.

'Brute Force and Ignorance'
Follows 'Shin Kicker'
As overhead sound to light floods on.

The hall erupts as stage is rushed
Bouncers do their job
10,000 watts of Marshal amplification versus bouncers in the
    Ulster Hall
All one can hear is 'A Souped-up Ford'.

'Moonfield' follows next — A lull in the storm
Rory breaks a string — not for long
'Too Much Alcohol' to go.

The end has come — the band leave the stage
The crowd chant 'We want Rory'
Back they come this time it's 'Hands off' and 'Fuel to the Fire'
The final encore.

Slowly the fagged audience files out feeling slightly battered
    but exhilarated
Out onto the cold dreary street — Bedford Street Belfast.
Policemen lean against Land Rovers eating hamburgers
Guns propped under their arms
Distant radio crackle audible
Sounding not a bit like Rory's lead runs
Walking into Donegall Square a saracen followed by a pig
    hurtled by
Blaring music of another kind.
A bomb goes off somewhere in the city
We're back to 20th century civilisation.

Patrick Gibson (13)
Dalriada School, Ballymoney.

The Divided City

This small city of ours,
Is usually so peaceful and quiet,
But not on a Saturday evening.
Then, it's the scene of riots.

This small city of ours,
Is ripped apart by two
Armies of supporters,
One red, one blue.

This small city of ours,
The home of two great teams,
On Saturdays it becomes
The home of horrible scenes.

This small city of ours
Has only some peaceful Saturdays;
They are only when
Either team is playing away.

John White (13)
St. Colman's College, Newry.

Where are my Dark Glasses?

And I left them at home along with a badge,
Life changed when the door bell rang
I was a member
But then so were they — of a 'better sort'? No.
I was glad to hear it was his knee,
And I gave a warning ...... Maybe

Ten years of sitting on a boiling pot,
Then it boiled, soiled, spewed and grasped,
Till I was here with these four dead walls and a beret
I was one of them, he was the other side
But then that's what it's all about
Paramilitaries
Planted something that grew outwards,
Far outwards — for a bomb is powerful you know
I had documents from command in a box for nine long years
And I threw stones
And I fired shots
And daubed walls and broke windows
And kidnapped
And planted bombs
And, And. I'm a member.

Kevin McGovern (14)
Rathmore Grammar School, Belfast.

Our thanks go to the following young people for the photographs used in this book:
Alan Rodgers and Charlie Whan (Annadale Grammar School), Judith Nesbitt (Dungannon High School for Girls), Derek Craig, Dennis Lyness, Joe Maginn, Jo-Ann Nelson, John Quaile, and Elizabeth Swain (Lurgan Technical College), and Pauline Wilkinson (Princess Gardens School).